Amazing and Fantastic

Ivy's ∧ Journal

A Trip to the Yucatán

Adams 12 Five Star Schools
1500 E 128th Avenue
Thornton, CO 80241
(720) 972-4000

Ivy's Journal

A Trip to the Yucatán

by Judith Herbst

pictures by Molly O'Gorman

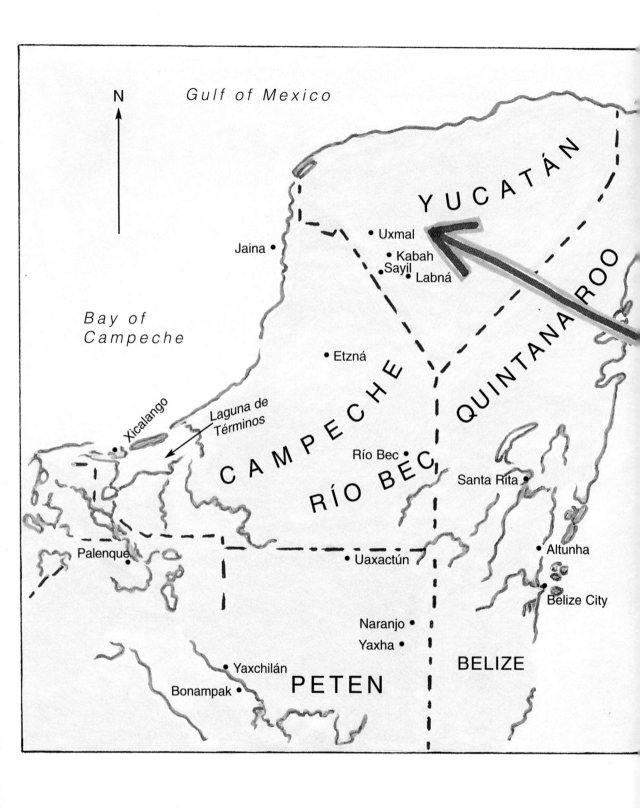

July 24

    I think my parents are nuts. They want to go to the Yucatán in Mexico and dig up pyramids. No. Change that. They already are going to the Yucatán, and I have to go with them! The trip is in three days. My dad says it'll be lots of fun. Oh, sure. Like I have nothing better to do this summer. I hope they don't expect me to learn Spanish.

This is where we're going!

July 25

At dinner tonight, my dad tried to start a discussion about Mayan Indians. He said that over a thousand years ago, the Maya built great stone cities in the jungles of Mexico and Central America. Now the cities are in ruins, and a lot of the palaces are buried.

"Serves them right," I said, "for building in the jungle."

My dad made a face but kept going. "The Maya lived in the cities for a long time," he said. "Then they abandoned them. No one knows why."

"Are the cities haunted?" I wanted to know.

"Oh, gosh, I hope not!" said my mother.

Too bad.

orchid grows upside down on trees

Things to take
1. sandals
2. shorts— the blue ones
3. white shirt purple

palm tree

July 26

I found some stuff about the Maya on the Internet, but
I sort of had to. My parents were really bugging me. There
were a lot of pictures of pyramids, and they actually
looked kind of cool. But there was also a picture of a
woman named Anne Cary Maudslay, who went to the
Yucatán in the 1800s. I thought that was pretty amazing
because women didn't do that sort of thing in those days.
Anne had to sleep in the jungle with bugs and snakes
and no toilet. And in the picture, she's wearing a long skirt
and carrying a parasol! How cool is that? I downloaded
her picture. I figure if Anne Cary Maudslay can do it, so
can I. We leave tomorrow.

July 27

We're here! We landed in the city of Mérida around 1:30 in the afternoon and then had to drive pretty far to get to our hotel. The cabdriver chattered to us in Spanish as he pointed at sights through the window. My parents nodded and said "Sí" a lot, like they understood. I'm sure the cabdriver wasn't fooled for a minute.

Our hotel is called Hacienda Uxmal. Hacienda means "farm" or "plantation," so I guess I was expecting horses, but there aren't any. Lucky thing there's a pool because it's really hot and humid here. Too bad this place wasn't around for Anne Maudslay, who probably had to sleep in a tree. Tomorrow we're going to see the ruins at Uxmal. I sure hope they're air-conditioned.

Our
room
(I think!)

Me!

Mom
and Dad

Hacienda Uxmal

July 28

Uxmal turned out to be right across the street from our hotel. It also turns out that I've been saying it wrong. It's pronounced <u>Ooooosh-maaal</u>.

Well, anyway, Uxmal was pretty cool. It's not like being in a museum where you can't touch anything. At Uxmal, they let you climb on whatever you want.

Our guide told us that 20,000 people once lived there, but almost all the buildings that are left were for the priests. Some of the buildings have funny names. One building is called the Nunnery, even though it never had any nuns in it.

the Nunnery

our
guide!

The best thing at Uxmal was the Pyramid of the Magician. My mom said it's a good example of what happens when you let stuff pile up in your room. Ha, ha. Very funny.

Pyramid of the Magician

The pyramid started out as a temple. But when it fell apart, the people figured the easiest thing to do was to just build a new one right on top of it. The more temples they built, the bigger the whole thing became until they wound up with a gigantic pyramid. The first temple is still in there, but the only way to get to it is through a tunnel.

The pyramid has 118 steps, and boy, are they steep! You have to sort of crawl up. But once you get to the top, it's awesome!

The guide told us that Mayan priests were still making offerings in the inner temple until around 1650. Can you imagine? Walking through that pitch black tunnel with maybe only a candle . . . chanting a language nobody understands anymore . . . burning incense in front of an idol. Wow!

incense burner

My parents, of course, took a gazillion pictures and asked about eight million questions. I didn't know what to ask, so I just kept quiet. After a while, I wandered off to check out the ball court.

The ball court is a great big open space, like a football field, but it has high, sloping walls on both sides and a ring in each wall. Nobody knows how the game was played. The rings don't stick out like basketball hoops. They look more like something you'd attach a net to, only they're about 20 feet off the ground.

Here's the temple. I'll bet the priests watched the game from up here.

This is one of the ball courts.

So there I was, kind of just wondering about it, when someone behind me whispered, "They sacrificed the winners, you know."

I spun around and saw an old man.

"They did?" I squeaked. I don't know why, but suddenly my heart started pounding.

The man nodded very slowly. He took a step closer. "The priests cut out their hearts," he whispered. "Como este, like this." He made a slashing motion at his chest, and I almost jumped ten feet. "Then they placed the beating hearts on an altar for Chaac, the god of rain."

"Oh, my gosh!" I cried. "They did that to the winners?"

"It would have been a great honor," said the man.

"Not for me," I told him. "I would have headed for the jungle."

July 29

Today we went to Kabah. We had to take a jeep because Kabah is in the middle of the jungle. The "road" was just a couple of ruts, and we got bounced around pretty good. But then an amazing thing happened. When we were about halfway there, we drove through a huge cloud of monarch butterflies. It was beautiful! There must have been thousands of them!

We passed a few huts that looked like this:

Little kids were watching us from the doorways. Our guide told us that the Indians who live here are descendants of the Maya. Their houses are just like the ones the Maya lived in 1,200 years ago.

There weren't any toilets, so we had to go in the jungle. No. Excuse me. There was a toilet, but it turned out to be a big trench surrounded on three sides by giant banana leaves. Well, I took one look at it and said, forget it! So my mom gave me some tissues, and I walked a little ways into the jungle. I thought of Anne Maudslay and decided she would have been proud of me.

Most of the buildings at Kabah are buried. The biggest palace is called Codz Poop. Don't ask me what it means. Anyway, the walls of Codz Poop are decorated with carvings of Chaac, who had the most gigantic nose! Maybe Codz Poop means "Palace of the Noses."

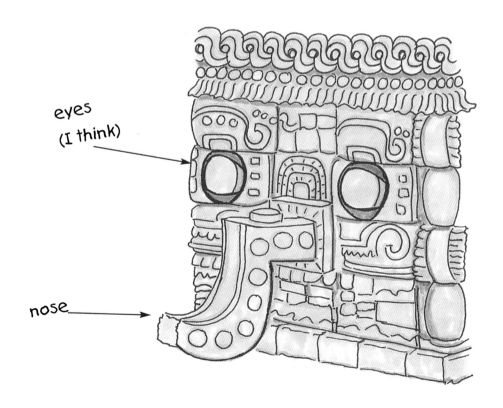

eyes
(I think)

nose

Seeing Chaac made me think of the old man and what he said about the priests sacrificing people so they would get rain. I looked around Codz Poop for bloodstains, but I didn't see any. Maybe the priests did such a good job, the rain washed them all away.

a Mayan priest

July 30

Today we went to Sayil. That's where my parents are going to dig up pyramids. Sayil means "place of the leaf-cutter ants" in Mayan, but it's more like the place of the killer mosquitoes.

There's not a whole lot to see. The archeologists dug out some of the buildings, but they're getting overgrown again. It's like the jungle is eating them. The weirdest one is called El Mirador. It means "the look-out."

I had the strangest feeling when I was there. I felt that if I stepped inside El Mirador, I would go back through time.

Sayil is very quiet. Most of the tourists go to Uxmal. So while I was wandering around I imagined I was a Mayan. I thought of what the priests would look like in their feathered headdresses. There would be a big procession. Musicians would be playing flutes . . . .

El Mirador

I could hear the sound of a rubber ball slamming against the stone walls of the ball court. Spectators were shouting. The athletes would play to their death. The crowd would cheer the winners. I would be on the stone steps watching.

I would be beautiful, of course, with long, black hair. Then I would see Ramón. Handsome Ramón. He would be on the winning team. He would catch my eye and blow me a kiss. And, proudly, he would march to his death . . . .

July 31

We went back to Sayil, and my parents started digging.
There are a few other crazy tourists who are also digging. I
can't figure out why they want to do all that work. They're not
getting paid for it.

I dug for a little while, but it's hot and disgusting, and I
started to get really bored. I bet Anne Maudslay didn't do any
digging when she was here. Parasol or no parasol, she would
have died in the heat.

August 1

I tried to talk my parents into letting me stay at the hotel. I told them I wanted to go swimming, but they said it wasn't educational. Instead, they sent me off with some other kids to Labná. All these places are starting to look alike.

Our guide was really good, though. He showed us how to make rubbings, and we each did one.

You tape a big piece of paper to something that has hieroglyphics carved in it. Then you rub a crayon over the whole surface, and a picture of the carving comes out on the paper. So I got my first souvenir. All my parents came back with was mosquito bites.

My rubbing of Mayan glyphs
(The original is hanging in my bedroom!)

August 2

Sayil again. I borrowed my dad's camera and took pictures. There was nothing else to do.

Labná Arch

August 3

The hotel packed us a picnic lunch, and today my parents let me go over to El Mirador by myself. There was no one else around.

That was good because Ramón was waiting. He had managed to get away from the others, but they would be looking for him. He couldn't stay long because if they found us together, they would sacrifice me, too.

"I don't want to live without you!" I told him.

Ramón silenced me with a smile.

"Chaac must have his hearts so that we may have our rain!"

"Oh brother!" I said.

And then suddenly, I heard footsteps. "Hurry," I cried, grabbing Ramón's hand. "Into the jungle!"

August 4

I saw a girl watching me today while I was having my lunch. I was at El Mirador again. We stared at each other for a long time. Finally, I shouted for her to come over.

I knew she didn't speak English, so I patted the steps for her to sit down. She pointed to herself and said, "Tránsita."

"My name's Ivy," I told her. She smiled and nodded.

It was a little strange at first. I sat there talking to her in English, and she talked to me in Spanish. Neither one of us knew what the other was saying, but then after a while, we started to figure it out.

Finally, Tránsita stood up and made a motion for me to follow her. I wasn't sure what to do. "Wait. I have to tell my parents where I'm going," I said, but I don't think she understood.

"Vamos," she said, pointing to the trees. "Vamos alli."

So I vamosed.

Tránsita

I had no idea where Tránsita was taking me. We crossed the cleared-out area around the Pyramids, and soon we were running through the jungle. It was very hot and still. My parents seemed so far away, in another century, almost.

Ramón was with us, running for his life from the Mayan priests who wanted to cut his heart out and give it to Chaac.

Suddenly we came to a little clearing and there, in the middle of the jungle, was a hut with a thatched roof, like the ones I had seen on the way to Sayil. A dark-skinned Mayan woman was outside, working a loom made out of sticks and small branches.

"Está mi casa," Transita said. "Está mi madre."

The woman was actually making cloth! I didn't know people had to do that. I thought you just sort of went and bought it.

The design in the cloth was beautiful. "Wow!" I said. "That's so pretty! Muy bonita."

Tránsita's mother nodded and smiled, and I suddenly thought, Oh, gosh! I said something in Spanish, and they understood me!

Tránsita showed me her house, which was really just a big room with a dirt floor. There were little kids running around, and I figured they were her brothers and sisters. When they saw me, they stopped running and just stared. They looked just like the carvings of the Mayans on the walls of the ruins.

When I got back to the hotel, my parents were totally nuts. I thought they were going to kill me.

"Where were you?" they screamed.

I told them about Tránsita and the hut in the jungle, and my mother's eyes almost fell out of her head. And then all of a sudden, my dad burst out laughing.

"What a great story!" he cried. "Evelyn," he said to my mom, "this kid's going to be a writer."

August 5

They sacrificed Ramón today.

By afternoon it was pouring rain. The archeologists told my parents they would have to stop work until the end of the rainy season. So I guess we'll be leaving in a couple of days. I wanted to say goodbye to Tránsita, but I couldn't find her anywhere.

It's raining!

Poor Ramón!

Altar

August 6

We drove back to Mérida this morning. In the 1800s, Mérida was known as ciudad blanca, the "white city," because it was so clean. My mom said it was also because the people liked to wear white clothing. They still do.

The men wear a pleated shirt called a guayabera, and the women wear a huipil. A huipil is just a square, cotton dress with a hole cut out for your head, but it's absolutely beautiful! There's colorful embroidery all over it, and of course, I had to have one. Angela Harrison will just die when she sees it!

guayabera

huipil

August 7

Our last day.

"So what did you think of the Yucatán?" my mom asked me on our way to the airport.

I grinned. "Yucatán es muy interesante," I said. "Me gusto mucho. I liked it a lot."

"Habla como una Mexicana!" said the cabdriver.

"Gracias," I said. "Hey, Mom, maybe we could come back next year."

"Well," said my mom, "next year I thought we'd study Stone Age art in the caves at Lascaux in France."

Oh, great. Like I have nothing better to do than poke around some clammy caves! I just hope my parents don't expect me to learn French.

This book was written with love for the proud and beautiful people of Mexico.—J.H.

To Janice and Ron—M.O'G.

Photo Credits:
Cover, Judith Herbst
Page 2, © Justin Kerr
Page 10, left, Kenneth Garrett
Page 10, right, Judith Herbst
Page 12, Kenneth Garrett
Page 13, Kenneth Garrett
Page 28, © Justin Kerr
Page 29, Kenneth Garrett
Page 31, © Justin Kerr

The editors would like to thank Artemis Picture Research Group for their invaluable research.

For information contact:
MONDO Publishing
980 Avenue of the Americas, New York, NY 10018
Visit our website at www.mondopub.com

Printed in China
July, 2011, Prosperous Offset (Shenzhen), 11613
   11 12 13 14   PB   9 8 7 6 5
   10 11 12 13 14   SP   9 8 7 6 5 4 3 2 1

Designed by Mina Greenstein

ISBN 1-57255-804-0 (pb)   ISBN 1-57255-839-3 (hc)   ISBN 1-60175-628-3 (SP)

Library of Congress Cataloging-in-Publication Data
available upon request